D1452072

PORSCHE 911

TRIVIA BOOK

Uncover the History & Innovation
Year After Year

By Neal Harris

Please consider writing a review!
Just visit: purplelink.org/review

Copyright 2021. Neal Harris.

All Rights Reserved.

No part of this book may be reproduced or transmitted in any form or by any means, electronic or mechanical, including photocopying, recording, or by any other form without written permission from the publisher.

Bridge Press
Email us at: bp@purplelink.org

ISBN: 978-1-955149-05-1

TABLE OF CONTENTS

INTRODUCTION

There's nothing quite like the love gearheads feel for their favorite sports cars. These are the marvelous machines that likely left their fingerprints all over your childhoods, from drawings in notebooks to visiting your local dealership regularly just to catch a glimpse. From an early age, gleaming sports cars turned you toward a life of worshipping at the altar of the car.

For many, the Porsche 911 is the definitive sports car. It has legions of fans worldwide. This German icon is one of the most well-known vehicles on this Earth, sports car or not—and for good reason. The Porsche 911 has been produced for decades and has always been fast as lightning. It has also never strayed far from the original—if it ain't broke, why fix it? From a multitude of beautiful models to exciting races to thrilling appearances in movies to unforgettable commercials, the Porsche 911 has had an incredible history full of memorable moments.

This trivia book is dedicated entirely to the iconic Porsche 911 and the fans that have continued to revel in its glory through the years. It travels all the way back to the car's fascinating origins and follows it through over half a century of innovations and triumphs.

The quizzes in this book will test your knowledge of the Porsche 911 from its initial development until the present. Each of the ten chapters consists of twenty multiple-choice and true-false questions, with the answers on a separate page (and remember, no peeking!). Each chapter also features ten Fun Facts about the 911.

Car-lovers can use this book to test their expertise on everyone's favorite sports car. But even when you don't know the answers, you're sure to learn plenty of interesting facts about this legendary vehicle and how those at Porsche are constantly challenging themselves to make it even more impressive with each new iteration.

Like a racer speeding down the track, there will surely be readers who will want to challenge their fellow gearheads to see who knows the most about the Porsche 911's stats and records. A book like this will help you and your motorhead friends determine who is the biggest Porsche 911 fanatic of all.

Whether you're looking to challenge a car-loving pal to a battle of wits, learn something new about the 911, or simply revel in the nostalgia of over half a century of this icon's history, you're sure to end up feeling even closer to your favorite sports car.

The statistics and information gathered for this book are up to date as of the beginning of 2021. The brilliant folks at Porsche are sure to keep coming out with new innovations for the 911 in the coming years and continue breaking records on the racetrack. But this book will give you more than enough knowledge to become a Porsche 911 expert.

CHAPTER 1:

ORIGINS & HISTORY

1. The Porsche 911 was developed as a more comfortable, larger, and more powerful replacement for which model?

   a. 287
   b. 459
   c. 356
   d. 585

2. The very first 911 model had the trademark shape of the side windows that has remained to this day.

   a. True
   b. False

3. The 911 debuted at the Frankfurt Motor Show in 1963.

   a. True
   b. False

4. The 911 was originally designated by which number?

   a. 901
   b. 903
   c. 905
   d. 907

5. Which French automobile manufacturer opposed the 911's original designation because it claimed a patent on car names consisting of three numbers with a zero in the middle?

    a. Renault

    b. Peugeot

    c. Citroën

    d. Alpine

6. The 911 was introduced in December 1963.

    a. True

    b. False

7. When were the first 911s exported to the US?

    a. March 1964

    b. September 1964

    c. February 1965

    d. June 1965

8. Which iconic car was introduced in the same year as the 911?

    a. Lamborghini Miura

    b. Range Rover

    c. Ford Mustang

    d. Citroen DS

9. How much did the first 911 model cost when it was released in the United States?

    a. $4,000

    b. $5,500

c. $6,750

d. $7,250

10. Due to shortages, Porsche was forced to use parts found with which iconic model to be able to fulfill their orders?

   a. Mercedes-Benz 770
   b. Audi Type T
   c. BMW 328
   d. Volkswagen Beetle

11. The Porsche 912 was meant to be a cheaper version of the 911.

   a. True
   b. False

12. What was the name of the more powerful 160hp car that was introduced as the first variation of the 911 in 1966?

   a. 911H
   b. 911J
   c. 911P
   d. 911S

13. The 1972 911 Carrera RS 2.7's distinctive *ducktail* was the world's first rear spoiler fitted as standard to a production vehicle.

   a. True
   b. False

14. What was the model year of the first 911 Cabriolet?

a. 1983
b. 1985
c. 1987
d. 1988

15. Though it was still recognizable as a 911 when it rolled off the line in 1989, the 964 had been reworked to such a level that it was considered over 95% new.

   a. True
   b. False

16. The last of the air-cooled 911s are from the 997 generation.

   a. True
   b. False

17. What year did Porsche introduce a new 911 model that had a liquid-cooled engine?

   a. 1992
   b. 1994
   c. 1998
   d. 1999

18. Which of these was the first production car to feature carbon-ceramic brakes?

   a. 911 GT2
   b. 911 Carrera RS
   c. 911T
   d. 911 SC Targa

19. In 2001, the Porsche 911 GT2 debuted with a top

track speed of 180 mph.

   a. True

   b. False

20. Where did Porsche debut the eighth-generation Porsche 911?

   a. New York, New York

   b. Milan, Italy

   c. Paris, France

   d. Los Angeles, California

ANSWERS

1. C – 356
2. True
3. True
4. A – 901
5. B – Peugeot
6. False
7. C – February 1965
8. C – Ford Mustang
9. B – $5,500
10. D – Volkswagen Beetle
11. True
12. D – 911S
13. True
14. A – 1983
15. False
16. False
17. C – 1998
18. A – 911 GT2
19. False
20. D – Los Angeles, California

FUN FACTS

1. The Porsche 911 was designed by Ferdinand Alexander Porsche, grandson of Ferdinand Porsche, the company's founder. Ferdinand Porsche was known for designing the Volkswagen Beetle. He also created the Lohner-Porsche (the first gasoline-electric hybrid vehicle), the Auto Union racing car, and the Mercedes-Benz SS/SSK.

2. The 911's beginnings trace all the way back to 1959, when Ferdinand Alexander Porsche made some initial sketches. Seven prototypes were built based on Ferdinand Alexander Porsche's original design and were internally referred to as the Porsche 754 T7.

3. In the short span of time between late August and early October in 1959, Ferdinand Alexander Porsche's type 754 T7 was produced. This car provided the foundations of what would eventually become the Porsche 911. The 754 T7's features already reflected those of the 911, which would soon be its successor. It had front-end styling and several other characteristics that were very similar to the 911.

4. The first one-to-one model of the Porsche 911 was made out of sheet metal and wood. On April 16, 1962, it was presented to the management board and accepted. The prototype was built that same year.

5. Ferdinand Alexander Porsche recalled of his father, Ferry Porsche (who was the chief engineer at the time), "When I was constructing the 911, he stood right behind me from the beginning. Not because I was his son, but because he was convinced. He always had a highly developed sense of form; he never liked extreme colors and forms."

6. When the 911 was developed, it was designed to feature a proof-of-concept twin-fan Type 745 flat-six engine. But when the car was introduced at the 1963 Frankfurt Motor Show, it had a non-working mockup of the single-fan engine. By February 1964, the car had an operational engine.

7. Officially, the early 911s already constructed with their original 901 designation were used for testing and exhibitions, and Porsche didn't sell any of them to private customers. However, several of the cars seem to have made it into the hands of private owners. In 1988, one was discovered and completely restored by Kurt Schneider and his wife, Lori.

8. Since the very beginning, every Porsche 911 has been made in one place—the main factory in Stuttgart, Germany. This factory is where the very first Porsche production model was made and also where all Porsche sports cars and engines continue to be manufactured today. Both racing models and standard production models are all built on the same production line.

9. Since its debut, over one million 911s have been built. Porsche claims that over 70% of these vehicles are still roadworthy today. The millionth 911 is a Carrera S in the special color *Irish Green* that was produced in May 2017. It now resides in Porsche's collection at the Porsche Museum.

10. Distinctively, Porsche has stuck closely to the founding concept of the first 911 over the years. "But we have continued to enhance the technology of the 911, refining and perfecting the sports car," says Oliver Blume, the current Chairman of the Executive Board of Porsche AG, "that's why it remains a state-of-the-art and technically innovative vehicle. We have also been able to expand the model line very successfully through derivates."

CHAPTER 2:

MODELS

1. What year did Porsche introduce the Targa?

    a. 1964
    b. 1965
    c. 1966
    d. 1967

2. Targa means *plate* in Italian.

    a. True
    b. False

3. Which company designed the forged aluminum-alloy wheels first available on the 1967 911S?

    a. Borbet
    b. Lorinser
    c. Otto Fuchs KG
    d. AEZ

4. Which 1973 model was designed as a race car for the FIA Group 4 class?

    a. 911 Targa 4
    b. 911 SC
    c. 911 Turbo Cabriolet
    d. 911 Carrera RS

5. In 1974, the Carrera RS 3.0 cost almost twice as much as the Carrera RS 2.7.

   a. True
   b. False

6. When it was introduced in 1975, the 911 Turbo was the fastest production car in Germany.

   a. True
   b. False

7. In what year did Porsche introduce the first turbocharged 911?

   a. 1972
   b. 1975
   c. 1978
   d. 1979

8. The large rear spoiler on early Turbos was known as a what?

   a. Whale tail
   b. Tiger tail
   c. Beaver tail
   d. Peacock tail

9. For the 1977 model year, the Porsche 944 replaced the 912E.

   a. True
   b. False

10. In 1978, Porsche came out with a new 911 and reintroduced which designation for the first time in

fourteen years?

   a. B

   b. GTS

   c. SC

   d. RS

11. Originally, Porsche planned to replace the 911 with the 976 in 1979.

   a. True

   b. False

12. When did the first 911 Cabriolet make its debut at the Geneva Motor Show?

   a. 1980

   b. 1981

   c. 1982

   d. 1983

13. Which 911 was conceived by famed engineer Helmuth Bott in 1983 but didn't get manufactured until six years later?

   a. 993 Turbo

   b. Carrera GTS

   c. RS America

   d. Speedster

14. In 1984, what name was brought back for the first time since 1977?

   a. Carrera

   b. 964

c. Turbo

d. 993

15. The 1989 930 Turbo is the only Porsche to feature a five-speed manual transmission.

    a. True

    b. False

16. One of the exclusive options for the 1989 Porsche 911 Carrera Cabriolet 25th Anniversary Edition was a Silk Grey leather interior with black accent piping.

    a. True

    b. False

17. Which one of these features did NOT make its debut with the Carrera 4 in 1989?

    a. Coil springs

    b. ABS breaks

    c. Power steering

    d. PDK gearbox

18. Porsche introduced a Turbocharged version of the 964 series in 1994.

    a. True

    b. False

19. The 993 was the final incarnation of the 1964 air-cooled 911.

    a. True

    b. False

20. *Motor Trend* named the 997 911 GT3 the "best handling car in America" in 2006.

    a. True
    b. False

ANSWERS

1. B – 1965

2. True

3. C – Otto Fuchs KG

4. D – 911 Carrera RS

5. True

6. True

7. B – 1975

8. A – Whale tail

9. False

10. C – SC

11. False

12. C – 1982

13. D – Speedster

14. A – Carrera

15. True

16. True

17. D – PDK gearbox

18. False

19. True

20. True

FUN FACTS

1. The first version of the Targa featured a stainless-steel roll bar because automakers were worried about meeting safety standards. Porsche wanted to be able to satisfy certain safety requirements proposed by the US National Highway Traffic Safety Administration since the ability to sell 911s in the US was vital to the car's success. Interestingly enough, these safety restrictions caused Porsche to design a car that was truly unique.

2. The name *Targa* was inspired by the Targa Florio, a famous Sicilian sports car race. After several accidents (two of which were fatal), the race was discontinued in 1973. There were many more accidents during the 1973 race, and seven spectators were injured. That final dangerous race was fittingly won by a Porsche 911 Carrera RSR.

3. In 1978, the 930 was modified with a larger 3.3-liter turbocharged engine. In order to fit the intercooler, a new *tea-tray* tail spoiler was designed to replace the whale tail. Porsche got rid of the *Carrera* part of the name (which had only been included in the car's name in North American anyway) and just called the car the Porsche 911 Turbo.

4. A Cabriolet concept car made its debut at the Frankfurt Motor Show in 1981. Though four-wheel drive was included in the original body design, it

wasn't a feature of the production car. The very first 911 Cabriolet was launched in 1982 as a 1983 model. At this point, Porsche hadn't released a Cabriolet since the 1960s. 4,214 cars were sold in the model's first year, despite its high price which was comparable to the open-top Targa. 911 Cabriolet models are still available today.

5. In order to save roughly 150 pounds in weight, the 911 Carrera Club Sport (CS) did not include any power options, a radio, a rear seat, a rear wiper, sound insulation, undercoating, fog lamps, engine and luggage compartment lights, door pocket lids, a front hood locking mechanism, or a lockable wheel nut. Even the rear lid *Carrera* logo was removed. Porsche only produced 340 units from 1987 to September 1989.

6. In 1988, Porsche came out with 875 Targa, cabriolet, and coupe models of the Commemorative Edition 911 Carrera to mark the manufacture of the 250,000th 911. These cars were painted Diamond blue metallic with color-matched Fuchs wheels. They had a leather interior and a silver-blue silk velour carpet. Ferdinand Porsche's signature was embossed on the seats' headrests.

7. Many collectors and enthusiasts believe that the 993 is the best air-cooled 911 of them all. According to Car & Driver, "Porsche's version of the Goldilocks tale is the 993-generation 911, the one many

Porschephiles agree that the company got just right. It's an ideal blend of technology and classic 911 air-cooled heritage."

8. Internationale Automobil-Ausstellung (known as both the International Motor Show and the Frankfurt Motor Show in English) is the biggest motor show in the industry. It is held biannually and organized by the Association of the German Automotive Industry. It is where the Porsche 911 made its world debut in 1963, as well as many other 911 models including the 911 Turbo, the 997 GT2, and the 911 Carrera 4.

9. To celebrate the company's 70th anniversary and the end of the 991-generation production at the 2018 Paris Motor Show, Porsche presented its 911 Speedster Concept. This marked a return of the double-bubble design to the 911 after eight years. Only 1,948 models were produced, in homage to the year the original Porsche 356 was released.

10. The 2021 Porsche 911 has a few new features and is a striking Python Green. It includes options for the 930 Leather package and lightweight insulated glass, which were previously limited to the pricier Turbo and Turbo S variants. The car also features programmable GPS capability for the optional front-axle lift system that senses when to raise the nose at precise locations. The Sport Chrono package now includes a digital tire-temperature display that appears in the gauge cluster.

CHAPTER 3:

EVOLUTION OVER TIME

1. 911s today still include all but which one of these features of the first 911?

    a. Free-standing front wings
    b. Lateral lines
    c. Design of the fastback
    d. Impact bumper

2. When the 911 was initially developed, Porsche did not have a design department.

    a. True
    b. False

3. The first 911 models generated 110 hp (82 kW).

    a. True
    b. False

4. The new 911 introduced in 1966 bumped the power up to what bhp?

    a. 140
    b. 150
    c. 160
    d. 170

5. The E series 911s had the oil filler cap positioned behind the right-hand door.

a. True

b. False

6. What was the approximate weight of the 1972 911S?

   a. 2,315 lbs.

   b. 2,478 lbs.

   c. 2,673 lbs.

   d. 2,739 lbs.

7. For the 1974 model year, the ducktail was standard equipment for the Carrera in all markets.

   a. True

   b. False

8. What was the crankcase of the 1976 Carrera 3.0 made of?

   a. Magnesium

   b. Iron

   c. Aluminum

   d. Brass

9. In what year was the SC's 3.0-liter engine replaced with a 3.2-liter engine?

   a. 1977

   b. 1981

   c. 1984

   d. 1986

10. When the Porsche 964 was introduced in 1989, it was the first 911 to be offered with the new four-speed Tiptronic gearbox.

a. True

b. False

11. The 993 Carrera was the first 911 to have a five-speed manual transmission included as standard.

    a. True

    b. False

12. The first standard production Porsche with twin-turbos was the 993 Turbo launched in 1995.

    a. True

    b. False

13. The 996 Turbo's engine was derived from which 911 race car that won LeMans in 1998?

    a. 935

    b. 911 GT1

    c. 911 Carrera RSR

    d. 993 GT2

14. The 911 released in 1999 displeased many car enthusiasts since it featured a front end that was identical to which cheaper Porsche model?

    a. Boxster

    b. Cayenne

    c. Spyder

    d. Taycan

15. Inspired by the 993, the 2005 997 featured round headlights.

    a. True

b. False

16. The Carrera S came with 19-inch *Tiger Claw* wheels.

    a. True
    b. False

17. In what model year did Porsche fit the Turbo with a new seven-speed, double-clutch, automatic gearbox for the first time?

    a. 2006
    b. 2007
    c. 2009
    d. 2010

18. How much lighter was the 2011 997.2 GT2 RS than a regular GT2?

    a. 50 lbs.
    b. 100 lbs.
    c. 150 lbs.
    d. 200 lbs.

19. Porsche lengthened the standard 911 by 3.4 inches for the 991 generation.

    a. True
    b. False

20. What was the starting price of the 992 911 unveiled at the 2018 Los Angeles Motor Show?

    a. $255,000
    b. $265,000
    c. $270,000

d. $280,000

ANSWERS

1. D – Impact bumper
2. True
3. False
4. C – 160
5. True
6. A – 2,315 lbs.
7. False
8. A – Magnesium
9. C – 1984
10. True
11. False
12. True
13. B – 911 GT1
14. A – Boxster
15. True
16. False
17. D – 2010
18. C – 150 lbs.
19. False
20. B – $265,000

FUN FACTS

1. In the 1950s, Ferdinand "Ferry" Porsche jotted down his wish list for the successor to the 356 on squared paper. He wanted the new car to include: "2-seater with 2 comfortable jump seats. Rearview mirror integrated in the wings. Easier entry."

2. Work started at Porsche on the development of a fastback coupe in 1962. Ferdinand Alexander had been commissioned to design a car based on the T7. Instead of a four-seater, this coupe would be a two-seater with two jump seats. The new Porsche would have an air-cooled, six-cylinder motor with an overhead camshaft. It was also intended to achieve the performance of the 356 Carrera 2, which extracted 130 hp from the four-cylinder boxer engine and had a top speed of 130 mph.

3. The F series of 911s was produced from August 1972 to July 1973. For this series, Porsche moved the oil tank back to its old location behind the wheel since when the oil filler cap had been behind the right-hand door, customers complained that gas-station attendants would end up accidentally pouring gasoline into the oil tank.

4. Porsche had to make a number of changes to the 911 during the 1974 model year so that it would meet legislative requirements for both emissions and impact safety. To achieve higher torque, Porsche

increased the engine size to 2,687 ccs. New impact bumpers were also added to the cars to satisfy US crash-safety regulations.

5. In 1989, Porsche's chief exterior designer Pinky Lai reworked the 911 (internally designated as the 996). It was the first substantial change to the car since Ferdinand Alexander Porsche's original design in 1963. "The company was about to be sold to either Toyota or Mercedes," Lai said. "The only model they were selling was the old 911. Sales were dropping from 50,000 to 40,000, and a year later 30,000." Lai helped to save the company with his designs and went on to win many international design awards.

6. The first standard production Porsche with twin-turbos was the 993 Turbo, launched in 1995. It was also the first 911 to have permanent all-wheel drive. The car's 3.6-liter engine made its power grow up to 400 bhp. This caused several car enthusiasts to compare the 993 Turbo to the legendary Porsche 959.

7. In 2012, the 997.2 GT3 RS 4.0 was introduced with the biggest flat-six engine the company had ever produced. The resulting sports car had 500 bhp and was lightweight. Porsche was able to drop some pounds off the car by using a carbon fiber hood and plastic back windows. In the end, the car's weight came in at just under 3,000 lbs.

8. The 991 era was one full of 911 firsts. The 991 was the first 911 to be made largely of aluminum. It was also

the first production car in the world to have a seven-speed manual gearbox. The 991s were the first to feature torque vectoring systems as well.

9. In 2011, the 911 went through its biggest overhaul yet. The 6th generation 911 came out of a massive redesign with a more powerful engine lineup, an entirely aluminum chassis, and PDK transmission. The new generation also included cool high-tech features like electromechanical power steering.

10. At the Los Angeles Auto Show in 2018, Porsche introduced the eighth generation of the 911. A presentation of the 911's long, exciting history was shown, as well as 911s from every generation. The 992 (Porsche's internal designation for the 911's eighth-generation) has wide rear-wheel arches that were previously only available on high-performance variants. This generation has aluminum body panels and is 1.8 inches wider than its predecessor. But while it has many new features, the newest 911 pays homage to the original with a similar-looking front and dashboard.

CHAPTER 4:

KEY PEOPLE

1. Ferdinand Porsche's father, Anton, was a master panel-beater.

    a. True
    b. False

2. Before founding Porsche, Ferdinand Porsche completed an apprenticeship to work as a what?

    a. Baker
    b. Carpenter
    c. Barber
    d. Plumber

3. When was Ferdinand "Ferry" Porsche born?

    a. 1909
    b. 1911
    c. 1913
    d. 1915

4. In what year did company co-founders Ferdinand Porsche and his son Ferry first set up shop with 200 workers?

    a. 1943
    b. 1945
    c. 1948

d. 1951

5. Ferry Porsche founded the Porsche Design Studio.

   a. True
   b. False

6. Ferdinand Alexander Porsche was commonly known by what childhood nickname?

   a. Butzi
   b. Schnurrli
   c. Herzerl
   d. Wurzelchen

7. In what year did Ferdinand Alexander Porsche join Porsche's engineering office?

   a. 1955
   b. 1956
   c. 1957
   d. 1958

8. When Ferdinand Alexander Porsche's type 754 T7 was first being produced in 1959, the designer was only twenty-three years old.

   a. True
   b. False

9. Ferdinand Alexander Porsche designed the Porsche Type 804 Formula 1 racecar and the Porsche 904 Carrera GTS in addition to the 911.

   a. True
   b. False

10. Who was Porsche's head of bodywork during the 911's initial development?

   a. Leon Schmidt
   b. Edwin Komenda
   c. Ben Zimmerman
   d. Franz Luca

11. Anatole Lapine became Porsche's chief designer in 1965.

   a. True
   b. False

12. Dr. Wendelin Wiedeking was the first CEO of Porsche.

   a. True
   b. False

13. Who was the first American to run Porsche?

   a. Joseph Abrams
   b. Harold Frieden
   c. Samuel Tasch
   d. Peter Schutz

14. In 1989, which CEO pulled the plug on Porsche's plans for the 965, a 911 powered by a rear-mounted water-cooled V8?

   a. Hans Klein
   b. Ulrich Bez
   c. Klaus Werner
   d. Kurt Lehmann

15. Dr. Wendelin Wiedeking was the head of production and materials management at Porsche before he became the chairman of Porsche AG.

    a. True
    b. False

16. In 2003, August Achleitner took over responsibility for the 911 model series.

    a. True
    b. False

17. Who has been the head of Porsche's design department since 2004?

    a. David Fischer
    b. Robert Hoffmann
    c. Michael Mauer
    d. Scott Wolf

18. At the beginning of 2019, Frank-Steffen Walliser took over responsibility for the 911 and which other car?

    a. 718
    b. 424
    c. 296
    d. 839

19. Current CEO Oliver Blume graduated from an international trainee program with which German car manufacturer?

    a. BMW
    b. Audi

c. Mercedes-Benz

d. Opel

20. In 2020, Oliver Blume indicated that a 100% battery-powered 911 would be introduced in the near future.

a. True

b. False

ANSWERS

1. True

2. D – Plumber

3. A – 1909

4. C – 1948

5. False

6. A – Butzi

7. D – 1958

8. True

9. True

10. B – Edwin Komenda

11. False

12. False

13. D – Peter Schutz

14. B – Ulrich Bez

15. True

16. False

17. C – Michael Mauer

18. A – 718

19. B – Audi

20. False

FUN FACTS

1. In 1900, Ferdinand Porsche invented the first functional hybrid gasoline-electric car at the age of twenty-five. Instead of using a battery, Porsche used a combustion engine to supply the wheel hub with electrical energy. But the car was extremely heavy, and its lack of infrastructure and short-range unfortunately did little to increase people's enthusiasm for electromobility.

2. Born in 1909, Ferdinand Anton Ernst Porsche inherited his three names from his father, grandfather, and uncle. His nickname "Ferry" was unusual since men with the name Ferdinand were more often called "Ferdy." But his parents thought of Ferdy as a common coachman's nickname, a profession that the family business had made obsolete.

3. The day Ferry Porsche was born, his father was competing in a race at the Semmering Pass in Austria. He drove in an Austro-Daimler Maja racecar that he had engineered himself and finished first in his class. He found out that his son had been born by telegram.

4. Three years before Ferdinand Alexander Porsche began work on what would eventually become the 911, Ferry Porsche had promoted Erwin Komenda to chief engineer. It was expected that Komenda, who

had designed the body of the Porsche 356, would develop the form of the 356's successor. But Komenda refused to follow Ferdinand Alexander's design. Ultimately, Ferry Porsche ended up having to take his son's model to be finished by an outside contractor that the company had recently acquired.

5. Anatole Lapine was Porsche's chief designer under two very different CEOs and was a close friend of Ferry Porsche for thirty years. He worked on the G series of the 911 — the model that succeeded the original 911. He designed the impact-absorbing surfaces and bellows for the American version. He made several changes to the 911: matte black window frames and door handles, fewer chrome ornaments, and a rear spoiler framed by jet-black rubber.

6. When Charles Schutz became CEO in 1981, he was displeased with Porsche's choice to cancel the 911. "The decision didn't sit well with me," Schutz said. "While the car could be temperamental at times, at least it had character. That's what people loved most about it." During a meeting in the lead engineer's office, he noticed a chart that depicted the development trends of the 911, 928, and 944. While the graph showed many more years of production for the 928 and 944, the 911's line stopped in 1981. Schutz grabbed a marker off the engineer's desk and extended the 911 line across the page, onto the wall, and out the door. He's now credited with saving both

the 911 and the company.

7. In 1989, Harm Lagaay took over as lead designer. He had already done work on the 993, 996, and 997 in addition to the Boxster, Cayman, and Cayenne. When designing the 996, Lagaay used the front portion of the Boxster. This angered 911 enthusiasts, who derisively called the car's headlights "fried eggs."

8. After training as a mechanical engineer, August Achleitner started out working on chassis development at Porsche in 1983. Having taken over responsibility for the 911 model series in 2001, he said, "The radiance of the 911 always fascinated me — its unique form and the concept. I have always been driven by the aim of preserving those aspects while nonetheless making everything better — and that approach has challenged me time and again."

9. After Ferdinand Alexander Porsche's death in 2012, Matthias Müller (the president and CEO of Porsche at the time) said, "We mourn the death of our partner, Ferdinand Alexander Porsche. As the creator of the Porsche 911, he established a design culture in our company that has shaped our sports cars to this very day. His philosophy of good design is a legacy to us that we will honor for all time."

10. Porsche's designers always begin their research by looking back at the past — and especially at the 911. After all these years, Porsche cars continue to feature trademarks like round instruments with the

tachometer in the center. Designer Thorsten Klein has said, "The 911 is our reference for every new development."

CHAPTER 5:

SALES & MARKETING

1. The 911 Targa was an instant hit when it made its debut in 1965.

   a. True
   b. False

2. Many of those who worked in Porsche's sales department worried that the Carrera RS 2.7 would be a failure, since initially, it couldn't be used as anything but a race car in America.

   a. True
   b. False

3. How many orders were taken for the Carrera RS 2.7 when the Paris Auto Show opened in 1972?

   a. 20
   b. 30
   c. 40
   d. 50

4. A Porsche print ad from the 80s asked, "Honestly now, did you spend your youth dreaming about someday owning a Nissan" or which type of car?

   a. Toyota
   b. Mitsubishi

c. Subaru

d. Honda

5. How many 911 SC units did Porsche sell in total?

    a. 37,285

    b. 40,193

    c. 58,914

    d. 64,029

6. Porsche's "Nobody's perfect" ad pointed out that Porsche won every place but one in the 1983 Le Mans race — which car won 9th?

    a. Sauber/BMW

    b. Lancia/Ferrari

    c. Rondeau/Ford

    d. WM/Peugeot

7. As of January 2021, the 911 is currently Porsche's bestselling car.

    a. True

    b. False

8. During the 964's five years of production, a total of how many units were made?

    a. 35,120

    b. 66,571

    c. 100,497

    d. 125,637

9. There was a famous ad campaign for the 993 Turbo with the slogan "Takes corners fast."

a. True

b. False

10. In 1993, what was the cheapest Porsche 911 on the market?

    a. Turbo S
    b. Speedster
    c. Carrera 2
    d. RS America

11. Which Hollywood actress appeared in a 1998 commercial as a daughter who kept missing the bus so her father would drive her to school in his 911 Carrera?

    a. Kristen Stewart
    b. Jennifer Lawrence
    c. Emma Stone
    d. Anna Kendrick

12. In which of these years was the highest number of 911s sold in the US?

    a. 1999
    b. 2000
    c. 2001
    d. 2002

13. In a 2005 commercial, a young boy is distracted in class by which car?

    a. 964
    b. 993
    c. 996

d. 997

14. In the past decade (starting in 2010), Porsche 911 made the most US sales in 2012.

   a. True
   b. False

15. Through the magic of film, which famous boxer appeared in Porsche 911's 2015 commercial, "Compete"?

   a. Mike Tyson
   b. Floyd Mayweather
   c. Muhammad Ali
   d. George Foreman

16. In the "Compete" commercial, grandmaster Sergey Karjakin challenges himself to a game of chess.

   a. True
   b. False

17. Which tennis champion rounded out the trio of fierce competitors featured in the original "Compete" commercial?

   a. Serena Williams
   b. Venus Williams
   c. Maria Sharapova
   d. Lindsay Davenport

18. A rare 1998 Porsche 911 GT1 Strassenversion went for $5.66 million when Gooding & Company sold it at an auction.

   a. True

b. False

19. What is the starting price of the 2021 Porsche 911?

    a. $74,300
    b. $99,200
    c. $105,600
    d. $117,800

20. The most expensive 2021 Porsche 911 is the Turbo S Cabriolet.

    a. True
    b. False

ANSWERS

1. False

2. True

3. D – 50

4. B – Mitsubishi

5. C – 58,914

6. A – Sauber/BMW

7. False

8. B – 66,571

9. False

10. D – RS America

11. A – Kristen Stewart

12. D – 2002

13. D – 997

14. False

15. C – Muhammad Ali

16. False

17. C – Maria Sharapova

18. True

19. B – $99,200

20. True

FUN FACTS

1. At the 1965 International Auto Show in Frankfurt, the 911 Targa was first introduced. In 1967, the model made its official launch. Despite current enthusiasm for Targas, the car did not sell well in its early days. Phil Skinner, the Collector Car Market Editor at Kelley Blue Book, said of the 911 Targa, "Initial sales were low; the car was impractical. But the early soft-top versions today can translate into a wow of a collector car."

2. One of the most famous cars of the 1965-73 generation of Porsche 911 models was the 1973 911 Carrera RS 2.7 coupe. Porsche produced the 1,000th RS on April 9, 1973. During the 1973 model year, somewhere between 1,560 and 1,580 RS models were built. The car got so many sales that Porsche was able to reclassify the RS for the Group 3 Grand Touring race category, in which the car went on to win many races.

3. A vintage Porsche 911 ad reads, "In Germany, there are no getaway cars" with a photo of a Porsche 911 police car below it. The ad points out that the car has the same engine that, when modified to power the Porsche 935, 956, and 962, won at Le Mans, Daytona, and Sebring. "Now, you'd think that would be enough to discourage any would-be offender in Germany," the ad goes on. "But occasionally, there

are still high-speed pursuits. They just don't last long."

4. The 964 was considered a sales success for Porsche. 15,023 units were sold in 1990. When the Turbo 3.3 launched in 1991, it sold well and helped bump 1991 sales up to nearly 22,000 units. In 1993 the launches of the Turbo 3.6, RS 3.8, and RS America were good for sales. The Turbo 3.6 sold well in 1994, as did the 964 Speedster. Overall, the 964 left Porsche feeling confident in the 911 as they began 1995 with the launch of the 993.

5. In Porsche's ambitious "Compete" commercial which debuted in 2015, Muhammad Ali, Maria Sharapova, and world chess grandmaster Magnus Carlsen face off against themselves.

6. Through impressive special effects, advertising agency Cramer-Krasselt was able to pit these legendary champions in their respective fields against their own doppelgangers. This commercial shows that the only car worthy of a competition with a 911 is the 911 itself.

7. In 2016, Cramer-Krasselt placed a special spread in 50,000 copies of the April issue of *Fast Company*. One of the pages in the spread included an acetate prism, along with directions for putting it together. The instructions told readers to visit 911hologram.com on their iPads, and then to put the prism on top of their tablets. While a video ran, viewers could see 3-D

footage of the latest 911.

8. Porsche only produced 23 units of the GT1 Strassenversion streetcar. They did so to meet homologation requirements so that the GT1 Evolution could race at the 1997 Le Mans 24 Hours. Chassis number 005 was reportedly only the second example produced and was originally bought by a German customer. In 2017, Gooding & Company sold the rare vehicle at a Florida auction for $5.66 million. At the time of sale, the car had 4,900 miles on it.

9. A Porsche commercial was broadcast during the 2020 Super Bowl for the first time since 1997. The commercial involves a chase between the first fully electric Porsche and several iconic Porsche cars, including the 911. As an Easter egg, Porsche included an unreleased 992-generation 911 GT3 in the commercial around the 43-second mark. The 2022 model has a big rear wing and major suspension changes but will retain the model's naturally aspirated 4.0-liter flat-six engine.

10. Macan was Porsche's bestselling car in 2020 with a total of 18,631 units sold. Having sold 18,092 units, Cayenne was a close second. 8,840 911s were sold, making the 911 the brand's top-selling two-door sports car.

11. The 2021 911 Turbo S starts at $203,500, and the Cabriolet version is $216,300. A lot of the exterior

colors are offered at no cost, but some of them are only available for an additional $3,270. If you want custom paintwork, that's $12,830. Exclusive Design wheels are $2,490, the Deviated Stitching Interior Package costs $4,490, and the Burmester sound system is another $3,980. With various performance-related options and vehicle assist systems, the most expensive Turbo S could carry a price tag of over $270,000.

CHAPTER 6:

MOTORSPORTS

1. Out of Porsche's over 30,000 victories on the racetrack, more than half of them were won with 911 cars.

    a. True
    b. False

2. The Carrera Panamericana ran from 1950 until what year?

    a. 1954
    b. 1957
    c. 1961
    d. 1963

3. Porsche won the Targa Florio in all but which of these years?

    a. 1956
    b. 1959
    c. 1961
    d. 1964

4. The 911 earned its first class win at the 1965 Monte Carlo Rally five months after it had gone into series production.

    a. True

b. False

5. In 1973, who was the first privateer to win an International Rally driving a 911 2.7 Carrera RS Sport (Lightweight) on the Circuit of Ireland?

    a. Mickey Grant
    b. Jack Tordoff
    c. Donnie Wesby
    d. Carl Barrand

6. The Porsche 911 Carrera RSR won all but which of the following races in 1973?

    a. Targa Florio
    b. 24 Hours of Le Mans
    c. Daytona 24 Hours
    d. Sebring 12 Hours

7. Jean-Pierre Nicolas won the 1978 Monte Carlo Rally with which 911 model?

    a. 953
    b. GT3
    c. 964
    d. SC

8. The 911 has taken seven titles in the European Rally Championship.

    a. True
    b. False

9. Porsche used 911-derived models to win the World Championship for Makes titles in 1976, 1977, 1978,

and 1979.

   a. True

   b. False

10. Karl-Heinz Quirin, Herbert Hechler, and Fritz Müller achieved Porsche's first overall victory with a 911 Carrera at the Nürburgring 24 Hours in 1984.

   a. True

   b. False

11. 911 ST cars did well at all but which one of these races?

   a. 500 km Tsukuba

   b. Sebring 12 Hours

   c. 1000 km Nürburgring

   d. Daytona 6 Hours

12. A 911 became the first GT Class vehicle since 1977 to win 24 Hours of Daytona in 2003.

   a. True

   b. False

13. From 2006 to 2009, which team used a Porsche 911 to win the Eifel Classic four times in a row?

   a. Wright Motorsports

   b. Orchid Racing Team

   c. Manthey-Racing

   d. Team Redline Racing

14. Between 2009 and 2015, a Porsche 911 GT3 took victory at the Spanish Rally Championship a total of

four times.

a. True
b. False

15. Which driver won the 2015 FIA R-GT Cup in a 997 R-GT rally car?

    a. Romain Dumas
    b. Marc Duez
    c. François Delecour
    d. Patrick Snijers

16. The Porsche 911 RSR scored a double victory at the 24 Hours of Le Mans after making its racing debut in 2013.

    a. True
    b. False

17. The 911 RSR was specifically developed for which race?

    a. FIA World Endurance Championship
    b. WeatherTech SportsCar Championship
    c. International GT Open
    d. GT Asia Series

18. What color was the 991.2 911 GT3 RS when it was unveiled in 2018?

    a. Tiger Orange
    b. Python Yellow
    c. Raven Black
    d. Lizard Green

19. The 2016 Porsche 911 GT3 Cup generated five horsepower more than its predecessor.

    a. True
    b. False

20. The customer team Wright Motorsports won first place with the Porsche 911 GT3 R in the GTD class at the 2020 IMSA WeatherTech SportsCar Championship.

    a. True
    b. False

ANSWERS

1. True

2. A – 1954

3. C – 1961

4. False

5. B – Jack Tordoff

6. B – 24 Hours of Le Mans

7. D – SC

8. False

9. True

10. False

11. A – 500 km Tsukuba

12. True

13. C – Manthey-Racing

14. False

15. C – François Delecour

16. True

17. A – FIA World Endurance Championship

18. D – Lizard Green

19. False

20. True

FUN FACTS

1. Up until the late 1960s, Porsche's involvement in motorsports was fairly limited. But even by the mid-50s, the brand had achieved success racing sports cars in the Carrera Panamericana and Targa Florio. Two well-beloved 911 models were eventually named after these classic races.

2. In 2003, Excellence Magazine named Lake Underwood "Porsche's Quiet Giant." Along with Bob Holbert, Art Bunker, and Charlie Wallace, Lake Underwood is identified by the Porsche Club of America as one of the car drivers who helped to make Porsche the "giant killer" in its early American races during the 1950s and early 1960s.

3. Three-time Formula One World Champion Jackie Stewart gave Nordschleife the name "Green Hell." It features changing track surfaces, plenty of tricky corners and steep inclines, and a layout like a roller coaster. The ADAC Total 24 Hour Race (also known as the Nürburgring 24 Hours, or the 24 Hours of Nürburgring) takes place over four days on both the Nordschleife and the Grand Prix circuit with up to 800 drivers racing with up to 200 cars.

4. 911s may be low-slung sports cars with rear engines, but that hasn't stopped them from having great success as rally cars. The 1973 Circuit of Ireland was won by a 2.7 Carrera RS Sport, and the 911 2.7 RS

Touring saw victory at the Donegal International Rally that same year. Even more impressive was Porsche's win at the Monte Carlo Rally in 1978. In that race, driver Jean-Pierre Nicolas took the wheel of a private 911 SC.

5. When driver Cathal Cathey first started rally racing in 1965, he entered the Circuit of Ireland with a Volkswagen 1500 and didn't do particularly well. But he later went on to win the 1973 Donegal International Rally, in no small part thanks to the 911 2.7 RS Touring he was driving. In 1974, Curley entered three International rallies with a 911 Carrera RS 2.7 Lightweight (or AUI 1500) and won each and every one. He also managed to achieve these victories in mechanically standard cars that had come right off the showroom floor.

6. It's not as hard to race for real as you might think. Director of Sales for Porsche Motorsports, Michael Dreiser, says all a person would need to have to be able to compete in the GT3 Cup is "the right racing license—this differs a little bit from series to series, based on whether they run on the international FIA calendar or purely locally—and the right car allowed in the series. This is usually the current model of the 911 GT3 Cup, but some series also allow previous models."

7. The Porsche 911 RSR, introduced in 2016, had a water-cooled flat-six engine with 4-valve technology.

The engine provided 346 kW (roughly 470 hp) — limited by a restrictor — that was transferred to the rear axle by a sequential 6-speed Porsche GT racing transmission developed specifically for long-distance racing. The paddle shift system gave the driver both a speed advantage and added comfort when changing gear.

8. The 2016 Porsche 911 GT3 Cup had a 3.8-liter six-cylinder boxer engine. With 460 hp (338 kW) at 7,500 revs a minute, the car extracted ten horsepower more than its predecessor. The rear axle delivered power via a race clutch and a Porsche Motorsport-designed six-speed dog-type gearbox with a mechanical limited-slip differential. Paddle shifts on the steering wheel were used to switch gears — a first in a Porsche Cup race car.

9. At the 2020 24 Hours of Spa-Francorchamps, the Porsche customer team Rowe Racing took the victory with the No. 98 Porsche 911 GT3 R. On the 7.004-km Formula 1 racetrack in Belgium, works drivers Earl Bamber, Laurens Vanthoor, and Nick Tandy were able to cross the finish line first after 527 laps. Matteo Cairoli, Sven Müller, and Christian Engelhart also conquered the 3rd podium place in an identical car.

10. According to Porsche, the 911 GT3 Cup is the world's bestselling race car. In 2020, Porsche introduced the latest generation of the GT3 Cup. It

can run on synthetic fuel and makes 510 hp (a whopping 25 more than its predecessor). In the 2021 season, the new GT3 Cup will be campaigned in the Porsche Mobil 1 Supercup and the national Porsche Carrera Cups in Germany, France, Asia, Benelux, and (for the first time) North America. The Cup car is the first racing version based on the current 992 generation. It is also Porsche's first makes-cup racer to feature a wide turbo-spec body.

CHAPTER 7:

STATS & RECORDS

1. The 1964 Porsche 911 could go from zero to sixty mph in 8.8 seconds.

    a. True
    b. False

2. How many seconds did it take the 1964 Porsche 911 to cover a quarter-mile?

    a. 16.2
    b. 17.8
    c. 18.4
    d. 20.5

3. How many seconds faster could the 1970 Porsche 911 go from zero to sixty mph than the 1964 911?

    a. 0.5
    b. 0.9
    c. 1.4
    d. 1.7

4. What was the hp of the 1989 Porsche 911 Turbo Limited Edition?

    a. 270 hp
    b. 300 hp
    c. 330 hp

d. 360 hp

5. The 1991 Porsche 911 Turbo could go from zero to sixty mph in 3.5 seconds.

    a. True
    b. False

6. The 1993 Porsche 911 Turbo 3.0 Coupé had a top speed of 160 mph.

    a. True
    b. False

7. For Turbo 993s, you could customize your order on Turbo S and GT2 models up to what hp?

    a. 434 hp
    b. 444 hp
    c. 454 hp
    d. 464 hp

8. Standard 996s got 3.6-liter engines in 2002, which added 15 hp to the naturally aspirated models.

    a. True
    b. False

9. Approximately how many seconds did it take the 2007 997 GT3 to go from zero to sixty mph?

    a. 3
    b. 4
    c. 5
    d. 6

10. Which model debuted at the Geneva Motor Show in 2013 with a top speed of 202 mph?

    a. 991.1 GT3
    b. 997.2 GT3 RS 4.0
    c. 991.2 GT3
    d. 997.2 GT3 RS

11. What bhp did the 2014 991 Turbo S have that enabled it to go from zero to sixty mph in 2.9 seconds?

    a. 500 bhp
    b. 520 bhp
    c. 540 bhp
    d. 560 bhp

12. The 2016 911 GT3 RS could speed through a quarter-mile in 11.2 seconds.

    a. True
    b. False

13. In 2017, Lars Kern drove a 911 GT2 RS around the Nürburgring Nordschleife in seven minutes and 3.4 seconds, breaking the record for the fastest lap around that track by a road-legal car at that time.

    a. True
    b. False

14. Approximately how much faster could the 2020 Porsche 911 Carrera S lap the Nürburgring than the Carrera S of the previous generation?

    a. 3 seconds

b. 4 seconds

c. 5 seconds

d. 6 seconds

15. According to 2020 market statistics, the Porsche 911 topped the classic and collector car auction market with $104.5 million in gross sales.

a. True

b. False

16. Which model was the biggest selling collector car of 2020?

a. 911 Carrera 3.2

b. 930 Turbo 3.3

c. 991 Speedster

d. 996 Turbo

17. With sales of $16.8 million, Porsche 997 was 2020's bestselling 911 generation on the collector car market.

a. True

b. False

18. In 2020, the fastest Porsche in production was the 911 GT RS.

a. True

b. False

19. As of 2021, what is the top track speed of Porsche's fastest 911?

a. 205 mph

b. 207 mph
c. 211 mph
d. 215 mph

20. As of January 2021, which is the most powerful car of the 992 generation?

    a. Turbo
    b. Turbo S
    c. Carrera
    d. Carrera S

ANSWERS

1. True

2. A – 16.2

3. D – 1.7

4. C – 330 hp

5. False

6. False

7. B – 444 hp

8. True

9. B – 4

10. A – 991.1 GT3

11. D – 560 bhp

12. True

13. False

14. C – 5 seconds

15. True

16. A – 911 Carrera 3.2

17. False

18. True

19. C – 211 mph

20. B – Turbo S

FUN FACTS

1. It may be surprising now, but in its early days, the Porsche 911 was not known for its straight-line acceleration. Its zero to sixty mph times were far behind several popular Italian sports cars and American muscle cars. But while the 911 wasn't as speedy as it would eventually be going in a straight line, it worked beautifully on a circuit from the start.

2. At the Paris Motor Show in 1972, the Carrera RS was introduced. It was the fastest 911 production car at the time and won several races. A lot of Porsche enthusiasts believe that it is the best 911 ever made. Many would go as far as to say that it's one of the ten best Porsches ever made, period.

3. The G series, produced from 1973 to 1989, included the first 911 Turbo. With a 3-liter engine and 260 hp, the Turbo had incredibly impressive stats for the time. It could go from zero to sixty mph in five seconds and speed through a quarter-mile in just thirteen.

4. The August 1989 issue of *Car and Driver* referred to the 1990 911 Carrera 4 as "the most technically sophisticated 911 ever to enter series production." The car's 247 hp made it incredibly fast and yet very easy to drive. It had the ability to go from zero to sixty mph in 5.1 seconds and to drive the quarter-mile in 13.6 seconds at 102 mph. Overall, the car had

a top speed of 157 mph.

5. When the 2007 997 GT3 made its debut, its top speed was 193 mph. It featured zero-lift dynamics to improve stability and had 415 bhp. In 2006, it only took Walter Rohrl, a test driver for Porsche, seven minutes and forty-two seconds to drive the car around Nürburgring.

6. With a 204-mph top speed, the 2007 997 GT2 was the first production 911 car to have a top speed greater than 200 mph. The 1998 Porsche 911 GT1 technically achieved this milestone earlier, but it doesn't count as a real 911 since it had a mid-mounted engine. It also wasn't really a road car since it was only built to meet homologation requirements.

7. In 2017, the Porsche GT2 RS broke a new record as the fastest production car at that time with a time of six minutes and 47.3 seconds on the treacherous Nürburgring Nordschleife. The Director of the GT Product Line, Andreas Preuninger, said, "It's not just the record time achieved by the GT2 RS that demonstrates the vehicle's class, but also its consistent performance in every lap."

8. The 911 GT2 RS claimed another track record at Road America in 2019. David Donohue, a factory driver for Porsche, made it around the four-mile track in just two minutes and 15.17 seconds. Porsche and the Wisconsin racetrack both have personal connections for Donohue, since back in the 1970s, his

late father had raced on the same track in a Porsche 917/30.

9. In 2020, the 991 was the 911's bestselling generation on the classic and collector car auction market. The 991 was in production between 2012 to 2019 and saw 159 transactions throughout the year. The end result was $23.2 million in sales. Many of these sales can be attributed to car enthusiasts' great fondness for the 991 Speedster.

10. The 2021 911 Turbo S has 640 hp and 590 pound-feet of torque. This puts the car at 60 more hp and 37 pound-feet more torque than the 991.2 Turbo S. It also has 197 hp and 200 pound-feet over the 2021 Carrera 4S. As a result, the 2021 911 Turbo S can go from zero to sixty mph in a lightning-fast 2.6 seconds — making it 2/10 faster than the previous Turbo S. It has a 205-mph top speed as well.

CHAPTER 8:

POP CULTURE

1. Robert Redford's character drives a red 1968 Porsche 911T in the film *Downhill Racer*.

   a. True
   b. False

2. What color is the 911 that Giovanni Ribisi steals in the first scene of the 1969 film *The Italian Job*?

   a. Blue
   b. Red
   c. Black
   d. Silver

3. Which actor drove a 1970 911 S in the film *Le Mans*?

   a. Burt Reynolds
   b. Michael Caine
   c. Steve McQueen
   d. James Garner

4. Jeff Bridges and James Woods' characters race against each other in a Porsche 911 SC and a Ford Mustang SVO in the 1984 movie *Against All Odds*.

   a. True
   b. False

5. Which famed stunt coordinator — who also worked on *The Lost Boys* and *Terminator 2: Judgment Day* — drove the 911 in *Against All Odds*?

    a. Gary Davis
    b. Hal Needham
    c. Craig Baxley
    d. Rick Avery

6. The 1987 film *No Man's Land* features a Porsche 911 SC, a 911 930 Turbo, a 911 Targa, and a Porsche 911 Flat Nose.

    a. True
    b. False

7. In *Bull Durham* when 911-owner Ebby Calvin LaLoosh receives one too many insults from his mentor, he says, "I'm the one driving a Porsche."

    a. True
    b. False

8. The Porsche 911 used at the beginning of the 1995 movie *Bad Boys* was on loan from which Hollywood director?

    a. Michael Bay
    b. Brett Ratner
    c. James Cameron
    d. Richard Donner

9. At the end of *Bad Boys*, a 964 Turbo 3.6 faces-off against which legendary muscle car?

a. Dodge Challenger
b. Pontiac GTO Judge
c. Chevy Chevelle LS6
d. Shelby Cobra 427

10. *Need for Speed: Porsche Unleashed*, a racing video game released in 2000, had cover art that featured the 996 Turbo.

    a. True
    b. False

11. What color is the 911 GT3 RS that Paul Walker's character test drives in *Fast Five*?

    a. Orange
    b. Green
    c. Blue
    d. Yellow

12. In *Bridesmaids*, Ted (played by Jon Hamm) drives a 993 Turbo.

    a. True
    b. False

13. In the 2013 film *Red 2*, Bruce Willis uses a 997 Porsche Carrera GTS for a car chase—but the car actually belongs to Jennifer Lopez's character.

    a. True
    b. False

14. A special expansion of *Forza Horizon 2* allows players to drive through Australia with various 911 models.

    a. True

b. False

15. Which actor finished second in the GTE amateur category at the 2015 4 Hours of Le Mans with his Porsche 911 RSR team?

    a. Rowan Atkinson
    b. Eric Bana
    c. Patrick Dempsey
    d. Matt LeBlanc

16. In 2016, which famed comedian sold a 1974 Porsche 911 Carrera 3.0 IROC RSR for $2,310,000 at auction?

    a. Jerry Seinfeld
    b. Eddie Murphy
    c. Jim Gaffigan
    d. Ricky Gervais

17. The 911 GT2 RS is the hero car of the racing video game *Forza Motorsport 7*.

    a. True
    b. False

18. Which 1989 964 model does James McAvoy drive in 2017's *Atomic Blonde*?

    a. Turbo S 3.3
    b. Carrera 4
    c. Speedster
    d. RS America

19. In 2019, Lego Speed Champions released a buildable toy car version of which 1974 911 model?

a. Carrera RS
b. Turbo 3.0
c. Club Sport
d. Cabriolet

20. Which character drives a 911 Turbo in the video game *Cyberpunk 2077*?

a. Viktor Vektor
b. Saul Bright
c. Dexter DeShawn
d. Johnny Silverhand

ANSWERS

1. False
2. D – Silver
3. C – Steve McQueen
4. False
5. A – Gary Davis
6. True
7. True
8. A – Michael Bay
9. D – Shelby Cobra 427
10. True
11. C – Blue
12. False
13. False
14. True
15. C – Patrick Dempsey
16. A – Jerry Seinfeld
17. True
18. B – Carrera 4
19. B – Turbo 3.0
20. D – Johnny Silverhand

FUN FACTS

1. The 1971 film *Le Mans* is almost a documentary with how it portrays the Le Mans 24 Hours race in France. While filming *Le Mans*, Steve McQueen drove his own black 911S in the movie's opening scenes. McQueen wanted to focus more on the film's cars than its actors — true to his vision, there is no audible dialogue in the film for the first thirty-seven minutes. McQueen's 911S was later sold for $1.375 million at auction in 2011.

2. The much-lauded 1977 film *Annie Hall* stars Woody Allen as Alvy Singer and Diane Keaton as the titular Annie. Christopher Walken plays Duane, Annie's brother. In one scene, Duane drives Alvy and Annie to the airport in a Porsche 911. Duane confesses, "Sometimes on the road at night, I have this sudden impulse to turn the wheel quickly, head-on, into the oncoming car." To this Alvy replies, "I have to go now, Duane, because I'm due back on the planet Earth."

3. Hollywood star Paul Newman raced in front of a huge crowd at the 1979 24 Hours of Le Mans. He drove a Porsche 935, which was derived from a 911 road car. Despite his rookie status, Newman (along with drivers Dirk Barbour and Rolf Stommelen) took first in the IMSA class and second overall. Adam Carolla bought that same race car for a whopping

$4.4 million at auction in 2016.

4. In the 1989 film *Weekend at Bernie's*, Bernie is shown standing in front of his 1978 Porsche 911 SC Targa while he romances his mafioso partner's girlfriend. After Bernie is killed by his partner, his two employees ride around with his dead body in a golf cart that looks an awful lot like Bernie's 911. When you're able to afford a Porsche 911 SC Targa, you may as well have a golf cart to match.

5. A 911 makes an appearance in the 2006 film *Cars*. Lightning McQueen's love interest, Sally Carrera, is a blue 2002 911 Carrera. She has a pinstripe tattoo on her back and is on a shortened wheelbase. Pixar's animators were given access to actual 911-series vehicles so that they could study them extensively. They worked meticulously to create a character who would move and behave as closely as possible to the real car.

6. The bright blue 911 GT3 RS in *Fast Five*—which Tyrese Gibson's character asks if the guys got from "Papa Smurf"—isn't actually a real GT3. It a 996 Carrera 2 with new wheels and a graphics package. Dennis McCarthy, the Picture Car Coordinator on *Fast Five*, said, "We didn't really have to do anything to the 911, it had plenty of power to do what we wanted. We welded up the spider gear in the rear differential so it would be locked and that was about it."

7. 2013's *Red 2* revolves around a retired FBI agent played by Bruce Willis and a ragtag group of elite operatives scouring the world for a missing nuclear device. In one scene, Katja (played by Catherine-Zeta Jones) performs a perfect 180 in her black 997 Porsche Carrera GTS and swings the door open. Then she slides over to the passenger seat so Willis can take her spot. A wild car chase through the streets of Paris with a Citroen 2CV ensues, and let's just say things don't turn out too great for the Citroen 2CV.

8. At Gooding & Co.'s Amelia Island auction in 2016, Jerry Seinfeld sold seventeen vehicles from his collection of Porsches and Volkswagens and walked away with $22 million. In addition to selling a 1974 Porsche 911 Carrera 3.0 IROC RSR for over $2 million, he also sold a 1966 Porsche 911 for $275,000 and a 1989 Porsche 911 Carrera Speedster for $363,000. The Carrera IROC RSR notably won the 1974 International Race of Champions, driven by racing legend Mark Donohue.

9. In November 2020, PUMA unveiled a limited-edition collection of shoes inspired by the eight different generations of the 911 Turbo. Porsche Cars North America's Vice President of Marketing, Pedro Mota, said, "To see the Porsche heritage so seamlessly translated into the design language of PUMA has been a thrill. Introducing a new generation of the 911 Turbo this summer was exhilarating, and working

with PUMA to celebrate the occasion has allowed us to share our sports cars beyond our core enthusiasts." Porsche Design's website held a special pre-release event on November 16th with an order window of 2.7 seconds, which is the same amount of time the 2021 Porsche 911 Turbo takes to go from zero to sixty mph.

10. Most of the cars in the 2020 video game *Cyberpunk 2077* are merely the inventions of the game's designers. But one genuine car in the initial release of the game is the Porsche 911 Turbo that Johnny Silverhand (played by Keanu Reeves) drives. Porsche partnered with Projekt Red to ensure that the in-game car looked and moved exactly like the real thing. In a fun bit of circularity, Porsche then wrapped a real 1977 911 Turbo so it would look just like the one from the game and displayed it outside the Porsche Museum in Stuttgart.

CHAPTER 9:

AWARDS & ACCOLADES

1. Which TV series gave its 1994 "Driver's Choice Award for Best Dream Machine" to the 1995 Porsche 911 Carrera?

    a. *Everyday Driver*
    b. *MotorWeek*
    c. *Speed Center*
    d. *Top Gear*

2. The 911 took 5th place in the 1999 Global Automotive Elections Foundation's Car of the Century competition.

    a. True
    b. False

3. In 2001, Porsche won *Popular Science* magazine's "Best of What's New" award for its Porsche Ceramic Brakes, which were an option available on the 2001 911 Turbo.

    a. True
    b. False

4. What year—which was fittingly also the Porsche 911's 40th anniversary—did *Autoweek* readers elect the 911 as "America's Best" sports car?

a. 1999

b. 2001

c. 2003

d. 2005

5. In 2004, the 911 was number four on Sports Car International's list of the "Top Sports Cars of the 1960s."

a. True

b. False

6. Where did the 911 rank on *Automobile Magazine*'s 2004 "100 Coolest Cars" list?

a. 1st

b. 2nd

c. 3rd

d. 4th

7. In the Automotive category, which 2007 911 model did *Popular Science* give its 2006 "Best of What's New" award?

a. Targa

b. GT2

c. Carrera S

d. Turbo

8. The 911 Carrera S won the "Best New Engine of the Year" award at the 2009 International Engine of the Year Awards for its 3.8-liter flat-six engine.

a. True

b. False

9. What year did *Motor Trend* name the 991 version of the 911 Carrera S as its "Best Driver's Car"?

    a. 2003
    b. 2006
    c. 2009
    d. 2012

10. In 2011, the Technischer Überwachungsverein's TÜV-Report determined that the 911 and which other car to be Germany's most reliable cars?

    a. Toyota Prius
    b. Kia Sorrento
    c. Hyundai Santa Fe
    d. Ford Fusion

11. The 911 S Coupe won World Performance Car in 2012, beating out the McLaren MP4-12C and the Lamborghini Aventador LP 700-4.

    a. True
    b. False

12. The Porsche 911 GT3 won the title of "World Luxury Car of the Year" at the 2014 World Car Awards.

    a. True
    b. False

13. The Porsche 911 Turbo S and which other 911 model made the Robb Report's 2014 list of the "Best of the Best" sports cars?

a. GT3
b. Carrera 4S
c. Targa 4
d. 50th Anniversary Edition

14. *Car and Driver* called the Porsche 911 the "best premium sports car on the market" in 2015.

   a. True
   b. False

15. *Motor Trend* awarded the 992 Carrera S with the title "Best Driver's Car" in 2018.

   a. True
   b. False

16. Which magazine gave the Porsche 911 a "Redesign of the Year" award in 2019?

   a. *Motor Trend*
   b. *Car and Driver*
   c. *Popular Mechanics*
   d. *Autoweek*

17. Which 911 model did Goodwood Road & Racing include on their website's 2019 list of "The 10 Best Porsches of All Time"?

   a. 930 Turbo
   b. 2.7 Carrera RS
   c. SC Targa
   d. GT3

18. At the 2020 World Car Awards, Porsche's 911 and

Taycan models were pitted against each other in the World Luxury Car category.

    a. True
    b. False

19. What was the 911's overall score in the Luxury Car of the Year category at the 2020 World Car Awards?

    a. 786
    b. 799
    c. 835
    d. 863

20. The Porsche 911 was named Luxury Car of the Year at the 2020 World Car Awards.

    a. True
    b. False

ANSWERS

1. B – MotorWeek

2. True

3. True

4. C – 2003

5. False

6. B – 2nd

7. D – Turbo

8. True

9. D – 2012

10. A – Toyota Prius

11. True

12. False

13. A – GT3

14. True

15. False

16. C – *Popular Mechanics*

17. B – 2.7 Carrera RS

18. True

19. A – 786

20. False

FUN FACTS

1. In 1999, the Global Automotive Elections Foundation—a jury consisting of over a hundred automotive experts—gathered to select the "Car of the Century." It's not terribly surprising that Ford's Model T came in first with 742 points; it's the car that jumpstarted the entire industry, after all. Next came Britain's Mini, with 617 points, as the runner-up, then the Citroen DS with 567 points, and the Volkswagen Beetle with 521 points. The Porsche 911 rounded out the Top Five cars of the century with 303 points.

2. *Sports Car International* gave a lot of love to the 911 in 2004. In addition to placing it at number three on its "Top Sports Cars of the 1960s" list, the automotive magazine also named the Carrera RS as number seven on the "Top Sports Cars of the 1970s" list. The 911 Carrera showed up at number seven as well, this time on the 1980s top sports cars list.

3. The prestigious Automotive News PACE Awards pay tribute to high performance in technological advancement, innovation, and business in the automotive industry. Porsche won two of these engineering awards in 2007 for the work they did on Variable Turbine Geometry and the High Energy ITM3e All-Wheel-Drive System with BorgWarner. Both features made their debut on the 997 Turbo.

4. *Top Gear* magazine selected the 911 as their "Coupe of the Year" in 2011. The magazine remarked, "...all things considered — its price, its performance, its economy, and its emissions — it's pretty clear we're talking about the world's best sports car here." Richard Hammond, co-host of the *Top Gear* television show, had also previously chosen the 911 GT2 RS as his favorite car of 2010.

5. In 2012, *Motor Trend* chose the sixth-generation 911 Carrera RS as its "Best Driver's Car." The magazine referred to the car as the "Best 911 Yet." The editor-in-chief of the magazine at the time, Ed Loh, said, "'Best Driver's Car' is the highest honor *Motor Trend* gives to a performance vehicle, which is the main reason it is so coveted across the industry. Congratulations to Porsche and its 911 Carrera S for beating out such a diverse, yet uniformly excellent field this year." The 2020 Porsche 911 Carrera S would go on to win "Best Driver's Car" in 2019 as well.

6. The Porsche 911 has taken the title of *Playboy* magazine's "Car of the Year" multiple times. The 7th generation 911 topped the list again in 2013. The magazine read, "Imagine a girlfriend who will be whatever you want, whenever you want — sexy, chill, an Olympian who can outpace Usain Bolt — and always exquisite. That's the new seventh-generation 911."

7. Every year a team of expert automotive journalists from sixty-nine different publications studies the vehicles released over the past twelve months and creates the prestigious list for the World Car of the Year awards. In 2014, the winners in each category were announced at the New York International Auto Show. While the Mercedes-Benz S-Class won "World Luxury Car of the Year," the Porsche 911 GT3 took home "World Performance Car of the Year."

8. J.D. Power, a company that offers data analytics and consumer insights, has been conducting its U.S. Vehicle Dependability Study for over thirty years. The 2019 study measured the dependability of 2016 model year cars, and the Porsche 911 achieved the highest ranking. It was named Most Dependable Model in the first year that such a title had ever been awarded.

9. At the 2020 World Car Awards, the Porsche Taycan won in two of the awards' five categories. It beat out the 911 for Best Luxury Car of the Year, and also in the Porsche-only Performance Car of the Year contest. In the Luxury Car category, the Taycan received a score of 846 while the 911 got 786, and in the Performance Car category, the Taycan's score was 867 while the 911 came in second with 809. The plan had been for the awards ceremony to take place at the New York Auto Show, but the show was delayed since the Javits Center was serving as a field

hospital for COVID-19 patients at the time.

10. *MotorWeek*, which began in 1981, is the longest-running automotive series out there. It also garners a great deal of respect in gearhead circles. The 911 has long been a favorite of *MotorWeek*'s and has been honored many times by the show's annual Drivers' Choice Awards. The 911 has won "Best Dream Machine" several times over the years—most recently the Porsche 911 Turbo took home the award in 2021.

CHAPTER 10:

ODDS & ENDS

1. What is "911" in German?
   a. Neunvierzig
   b. Neunsieben
   c. Neunzwölf
   d. Neunelfer

2. Which of these is a way to refer to the 911's car-body style of two front seats and two smaller rear seats?
   a. 2+2
   b. Double 2
   c. 2 on 2
   d. Front-jump 2

3. The driver's side mirror on the 911 is mounted a few inches further back on the door than the mirror on the passenger's side.
   a. True
   b. False

4. What year was the 912 discontinued?
   a. 1967
   b. 1969
   c. 1971
   d. 1973

5. Series F 911S models weigh 2,910 lbs.

    a. True
    b. False

6. How many 959s were produced in total?

    a. 175
    b. 292
    c. 384
    d. 427

7. The 964 included all but one of these new features that older models lacked?

    a. Bosch mechanical fuel injection
    b. Airbags
    c. Power steering
    d. Tiptronic automatic transmission

8. Mainly thanks to its poly-ellipsoid-shaped headlights, the front end of the 993 is lower slung than earlier 911s.

    a. True
    b. False

9. The first 996 models had naturally-aspirated engines that produced 257 hp.

    a. True
    b. False

10. Which standard 996 model was the 996 GT3 based on?

a. Carrera
b. Targa
c. Turbo
d. Turbo S

11. According to GT2 Class racing rules, the rear-wheel-drive variant of a race car has to weigh less than the all-wheel-drive option.

a. True
b. False

12. Out of the Top Five cars voted Car of the Century in 1999, the 911 is the only car that has remained continuously in production since its introduction.

a. True
b. False

13. What is the most commonly preferred color of 911s in the US?

a. Gray
b. Black
c. White
d. Red

14. The 997 Carrera S was unveiled in 2003.

a. True
b. False

15. The Porsche factory in Stuttgart manufactures how many 911s a day on average?

a. 50

b. 80

c. 110

d. 140

16. Approximately how many welds does each 911 have?

    a. 4,000

    b. 4,500

    c. 5,000

    d. 5,500

17. The Porsche GT3 wasn't available in the United States until 2004.

    a. True

    b. False

18. Newer 911s tend to be less fuel-efficient than previous models.

    a. True

    b. False

19. What year did the 911 GT3 make its US debut in New York with an increased hp of 435?

    a. 2009

    b. 2011

    c. 2013

    d. 2015

20. The 2021 911 Targa 4S is available in colors like Guards Red, Racing Yellow, and Lava Orange.

    a. True

b. False

ANSWERS

1. D – Neunelfer

2. A – 2+2

3. False

4. B – 1969

5. False

6. B – 292

7. A – Bosch mechanical fuel injection

8. True

9. False

10. A – Carrera

11. True

12. True

13. B – Black

14. False

15. C – 110

16. C – 5,000

17. True

18. False

19. A – 2009

20. True

FUN FACTS

1. While the Porsche 911 is a sports car — the best sports car there is, according to many car enthusiasts — it was definitely inspired by many aspects of the Volkswagen Beetle. This is not such a surprise considering that both cars were dreamed up by members of the same family. The Volkswagen Beetle was, in a way, the grandfather to the 911 since the former was designed by Ferdinand Porsche while the 911 was the brainchild of his grandson, Ferdinand Alexander Porsche.

2. Ferdinand Alexander Porsche was Ferry Porsche's oldest son. He was a designer for Porsche from 1962 onward. In 1990, he became the chairman of Porsche AG. During his time as chairman, he helped to ensure the company's future success after there was a decline in sales in the late 1980s. He died in 2012.

3. The 912 had a fairly brief production run from 1964 to 1969. In 1969, Porsche made the decision to discontinue the 911-variant. One of the reasons for this was because the production facility where the 912 was manufactured was needed for a new model, the 914-6. The United States had also begun to require stricter emission-control regulations, which meant that Porsche would need to do some serious reengineering of all their vehicles. With multiple 911s and the 914 to worry about, Porsche decided

that the 912 wasn't worth keeping around. "It would have taken some trouble to prepare the 912 for the new exhaust rules," Ferry Porsche said, "and with the arrival of the 914 we would have three different engines to keep current. That was too many."

4. Much to many car enthusiasts' dismay, the Sportomatic 911 model included an automatic transmission. Porsche argued that cars with manual transmission are difficult to drive through the stop-and-go of congested traffic. It seems that consumers agreed with Porsche's logic; despite all the complaints from gearheads, the Sportomatic 911 went on to sell well for over twenty years until it was discontinued in 1980.

5. Roaring onto the scene in 1986, the 959 was based on the 911 and had a top speed of 197 mph. Its tech was way ahead of its time, with an electronically-controlled chassis and a biturbo engine with water-cooled four-valve cylinder heads. The 959 also featured an all-wheel-drive system and a body that was aerodynamically optimized. In 1988, production of this wonder-car ended its limited run with just 292 cars in total.

6. Despite the fact that all-wheel-drive isn't something to get too excited about today, it was positively revolutionary when Porsche introduced an all-wheel-drive 911 Carrera 4 model in 1989. With it, drivers could be confident taking their 911s out on

roads with varying conditions. All-wheel-drive offered drivers greater control whenever their driving environment became harder to manage.

7. Under direction from CEO Wendelin Wiedeking in 1995, Porsche made the decision to discontinue their 928 and 968 models since they had proven unprofitable. They chose instead to double-down on the 911, working to overhaul the vehicle and revive the world's interest in the iconic car. This choice reshaped the company and helped save Porsche from the brink of bankruptcy. And to think, fourteen years earlier, Porsche had been ready to give the 911 the ax in favor of the 928.

8. In 2011, Porsche and the Williams F1 Team worked to produce the 911 GT3 R Hybrid 2.0, a hybrid race car. The GT3 R Hybrid 2.0 was so unique that racing bodies weren't sure how to classify the innovative machine in its races. The car had a top speed of 175 mph and could go from zero to sixty mph in just 2.5 seconds. During an American Le Mans Series race at Laguna Seca in September 2011, the GT3 R Hybrid 2.0 competed in an exhibition class and beat out the entire GT class.

9. One of the 911's most distinctive features is that its engine resides in the back of the car rather than the front. This sort of car design means that there needs to be higher tire pressure for the back wheels than the front ones to account for the car's uneven weight

distribution. So it's important to keep an eye on your 911's tire pressure since lower pressure in the back wheels can result in more wear on the tires. You'll also end up needing to fuel up more often.

10. Perhaps more than any other sports car, there's a 911 for every type of driver. There's even one for those who don't want to drive too fast — the 912, which has a top speed of just 116 mph. At the other end of the spectrum is the Porsche 911 GT RS, which has nearly double the top speed of the 912 at 211 mph. No matter what your personal tastes are, it's likely that at least one of the 911's countless iterations will make you drool.

CONCLUSION

You've just taken a road trip through the Porsche 911's history from its inception in 1963 through the 2021 992-generation over fifty years later, and you've encountered countless pieces of fascinating trivia and intriguing facts along the way. We hope the journey has been interesting and enjoyable for you and that it also helped to expand your knowledge of the world's favorite sports car.

We're sure a 911 aficionado like yourself was aware of at least some of this trivia already, but we tried to provide some little-known stories and fun facts about this iconic vehicle that you might not have come across before. More than anything, we wanted this book to provide an education on the Porsche 911's illustrious history, beautiful models, thrilling racing records, and many fantastic appearances throughout different facets of pop culture—and to do so in a way that was as fun and entertaining as possible. After all, an amazing car like the 911 deserves nothing less.

Hopefully, you will be able to take the information laid out here and challenge your gearhead buddies to Porsche 911 trivia battles. Then you can prove who is the greatest 911 fanatic of all. You could also share the history of the 911's origins and early racing triumphs with younger fans who may not be aware of it. Perhaps you could introduce them to older films like *Le Mans* and *Downhill Racer* that celebrate the sleek beauty of this iconic sports car.

The Porsche 911 has an extensive history full of gorgeous models, famous races, and Porsche employees behind the scenes who made it all possible. We're sure there are plenty of fascinating facts that we missed. But this book should provide you with a solid foundation of 911 knowledge, and will perhaps inspire you to dig even deeper on your own. No matter what, we can guarantee that you will already have a sizable start over your car-enthusiast friends when it comes to 911 trivia challenges.

The Porsche 911 is one of the most beloved sports cars in the world — possibly *the* most beloved sports car. It represents the proud heritage of the Porsche family, with grandfather, son, and grandson all having a hand in making the great vehicle it is today. Ferdinand Alexander Porsche had to fight to preserve the originality of his vision for the very first 911 and couldn't have done it without the support of his father, Ferry, at every step of the way. And there would be no 911 without inspiration from the Volkswagen Beetle, designed by Ferdinand Porsche.

While it was popular from the start, the Porsche 911 did eventually have a few slumps in sales. Porsche almost made the disastrous choice of discontinuing the 911 in 1981. Luckily, Peter Schutz, the CEO at the time, stopped that from happening. But it is the support of 911 fans like yourself that has kept the 911 going all the way from 1963 to today.

CPSIA information can be obtained
at www.ICGtesting.com
Printed in the USA
BVHW070112211221
624506BV00017B/1846